I'm So Gonna Crush My Goals

KNOCK KNOCK®
LOS ANGELES, CALIFORNIA

Created, published, and distributed by Knock Knock
11111 Jefferson Blvd. #5167
Culver City, CA 90231
knockknockstuff.com
Knock Knock is a registered trademark of Knock Knock LLC
Inner-Truth is a registered trademark of Knock Knock LLC

This book is meant solely for entertainment purposes. In no event will
Knock Knock be liable to any reader for any harm, injury, or damages,
including direct, indirect, incidental, special, consequential, or punitive
arising out of or in connection with the use of the information contained
in this book. So there.

Where specific company, product, and brand names are cited, copyright
and trademarks associated with these names are property of their respective
owners. Every reasonable attempt has been made to identify owners
of copyright. Errors or omissions will be corrected in subsequent editions.

ISBN: 978-1-68349-301-3
UPC: 825703-50198-8

10 9 8 7 6 5 4 3 2 1

YOU ARE #GOALS.

Truly. You're #goals because you *have* goals—lots of 'em: relationship goals, career goals, creative goals, health goals, home goals, hair goals, finance goals, space travel goals (hey, anything's possible). And that's okay. In fact, it's great. Goals are life-giving. Goals are golden.

It's been said that goals are dreams with deadlines, and that's the key to their power. A dream may be beautiful, but a goal can actually help you get there. And because a goal is more concrete than a dream, it's also easier to recognize when you've crushed it. Goals respond well to rough handling (speaking of crushing!); they positively *love* being broken down into smaller chunks.

One thing to know about goals, though. For every goal you crush, another will sprout up in its place. They just keep coming—along with those familiar pangs of panic and imposter syndrome that can plague even the most accomplished goal-crusher. Those feelings are normal, and you mustn't let them stop you from setting—and crushing—your many goals.

This journal can help with that.

As celebrated self-help author Deepak Chopra asserts, "Journaling is one of the most powerful tools we have to transform our lives." It helps to put one's mind at ease—essential for getting into the goal-crushing mental zone—and has even been shown to aid physical health. According to a widely cited study by James W. Pennebaker and Janel D. Seagal, "Writing about important personal experiences in an emotional way . . . Brings about improvements in mental and physical health." Proven benefits include better stress management, strengthened immune systems, fewer doctor visits, and improvement in chronic illnesses such as asthma. If it can help our lungs, imagine what it can do for our brains?

It's not entirely clear how journaling accomplishes all this. Catharsis is involved, but many also note the value of organizing experiences into a cohesive narrative. Sometimes, simply putting a name to a feeling can give us back a sense of power over our experience. According to *Newsweek*, some experts believe that journaling "forces us to transform the ruminations cluttering our minds into coherent stories." Writing about your life goals can help you clarify who you are and recognize which goals excite you at your very core.

Of course, tapping our inner power isn't a one-and-done deal—it's a lifelong process, much like keeping a journal. Specialists agree that in order to reap the benefits of journaling you should stick with it, quasi-daily, for as little as five minutes at a time (at least fifteen minutes, however, is best), even on days when you feel unmotivated, exhausted, or empty. Finding regular writing times and comfortable locations can help with consistency.

If you're not sure what to write about, use the quotes inside this journal as a jumping-off point for observations and explorations. Renowned journaler Anaïs Nin suggests asking yourself, "What feels vivid, warm, or near to you at the moment?" This is also excellent advice for figuring out what goals you want to pursue. To build your goal-crushing confidence, reflect on the many goals and accomplish-ments you have already achieved in your life, no matter how small. Consider also the numerous challenges you've overcome and difficulties you've survived; recognizing these should help bolster your sense of your own inner strength and perseverence. Write whatever comes to you, and don't criticize it; journaling is a means of self-reflection, not a structured composition. And since this journal is all about goal-crushing, you may also use it as a safe place to make lists and plot out step-by-step strategies.

Finally, find a special spot for your journal so it'll be easy to find on days when you're feeling at the peak of your powers, or (especially) on days when you fear all may be lost. Read your favorite quotes over and over and over. Tear them out and post them near your bed, or whip out your watercolors and turn them into art. Whatever you do, believe this: Your goals matter, and you deserve the joy of pursuing them with confidence and trust in your inner wisdom.

Now go forth and crush some goals!

I come in peace, but I mean business.

Janelle Monáe

How I'm Gonna Crush My Goals Today:

Inspiration is for amateurs—the rest of us just show up and get to work.

Chuck Close

DATE:

How I'm Gonna Crush My Goals Today:

....

....

....

....

....

....

....

....

....

....

....

....

....

TODAY'S LEVEL OF HUSTLE:

☐  ☐ ☐ ☐

My comfort zone is like a little bubble around me, and I've pushed it in different directions and made it bigger and bigger until these objectives that seemed totally crazy, eventually fall within the realm of the possible.

Alex Honnold

DATE:

How I'm Gonna Crush My Goals Today:

....

....

....

....

....

....

....

....

....

....

....

....

TODAY'S LEVEL OF HUSTLE:

☐   ☐   ☐   ☐

With tuppence for paper and strings, you can have your own set of wings!

Mr. Banks (Mary Poppins)

DATE:

How I'm Gonna Crush My Goals Today:

TODAY'S LEVEL OF HUSTLE:

Make the most of yourself by fanning the tiny, inner sparks of possibility into flames of achievement.

Golda Meir

DATE:

How I'm Gonna Crush My Goals Today:

....

....

....

....

....

....

....

....

....

....

....

....

TODAY'S LEVEL OF HUSTLE:

□   □   □   □

Victory is very, very sweet. It tastes better than any dessert you've ever had.

Serena Williams

How I'm Gonna Crush My Goals Today:

....

....

....

....

....

....

....

....

....

....

....

....

....

TODAY'S LEVEL OF HUSTLE:

☐   ☐    ☐   ☐

The question of your worthiness is not on the table at all. You know what you want. Embrace that and stand up for it without huffing the spray paint that everyone else is huffing.

Heather Havrilesky

How I'm Gonna Crush My Goals Today:

....

....

....

....

....

....

....

....

....

....

....

....

....

TODAY'S LEVEL OF HUSTLE:

☐   ☐   ☐   ☐

I never look back, darling! It distracts me from the now.

Edna (The Incredibles)

DATE:

—— How I'm Gonna Crush My Goals Today: ——

What you do every day matters more than what you do once in a while.

Gretchen Rubin

DATE:

How I'm Gonna Crush My Goals Today:

....

....

....

....

....

....

....

....

....

....

....

....

TODAY'S LEVEL OF HUSTLE:

If you're offered a seat on a rocket ship, don't ask what seat! Just get on.

Sheryl Sandberg

DATE:

How I'm Gonna Crush My Goals Today:

....

....

....

....

....

....

....

....

....

....

....

....

....

....

....

....

....

TODAY'S LEVEL OF HUSTLE:

The only place where success comes before work is in the dictionary.

Vince Lombardi

How I'm Gonna Crush My Goals Today:

....

....

....

....

....

....

....

....

....

....

....

....

....

TODAY'S LEVEL OF HUSTLE:

Said the river: imagine everything you can imagine, then keep on going.

Mary Oliver

How I'm Gonna Crush My Goals Today:

TODAY'S LEVEL OF HUSTLE:

□ □  □ □

And I pay my mama bills

I ain't got no time to chill.

Cardi B

— How I'm Gonna Crush My Goals Today: —

....

....

....

....

....

....

....

....

....

....

....

....

....

TODAY'S LEVEL OF HUSTLE:

☐   ☐   ☐    ☐

Never do anything by halves if you want to get away with it. Be outrageous. Go the whole hog. Make sure everything you do is so completely crazy it's unbelievable.

Roald Dahl (*Matilda*)

DATE:

How I'm Gonna Crush My Goals Today:

....

....

....

....

....

....

....

....

....

....

....

....

....

TODAY'S LEVEL OF HUSTLE:

☐   ☐    ☐   ☐

I am no bird; and no net ensnares me.

Charlotte Brontë

DATE:

How I'm Gonna Crush My Goals Today:

Burn, burn, burn like fabulous yellow roman candles exploding like spiders across the stars.

Jack Kerouac

How I'm Gonna Crush My Goals Today:

☐   ☐   ☐    ☐

Think like a queen. A queen is not afraid to fail. Failure is another stepping stone to greatness.

Oprah Winfrey

DATE:

How I'm Gonna Crush My Goals Today:

....

....

....

....

....

....

....

....

....

....

....

....

....

....

TODAY'S LEVEL OF HUSTLE:

I believe in my inner genius and encourage it to speak up as much as possible ... The more validated my genius feels, the more apt it is to participate. And nobody puts my genius in the corner.

Suzi Barrett

DATE:

How I'm Gonna Crush My Goals Today:

....

....

....

....

....

....

....

....

....

....

....

....

TODAY'S LEVEL OF HUSTLE:

□ zZ^Z   □   □   □

I never wanted to take the easy way, and I was always willing to hustle.

Bebe Rexha

DATE:

How I'm Gonna Crush My Goals Today:

....

....

....

....

....

....

....

....

....

....

....

....

TODAY'S LEVEL OF HUSTLE:

☐   ☐   ☐   ☐

If you have a goal that is very, very far out, and you approach it in little steps, you start to get there faster.

Mae Jemison

DATE:

How I'm Gonna Crush My Goals Today:

....

....

....

....

....

....

....

....

....

....

....

TODAY'S LEVEL OF HUSTLE:

You're strong, you're a Kelly Clarkson song, you got this.

Jonathan Van Ness

DATE:

How I'm Gonna Crush My Goals Today:

....

....

....

....

....

....

....

....

....

....

....

....

TODAY'S LEVEL OF HUSTLE:

☐   ☐    ☐   ☐

It's amazing what we can do if we simply refuse to give up.

Octavia Butler

DATE:

How I'm Gonna Crush My Goals Today:

....

....

....

....

....

....

....

....

....

....

....

....

TODAY'S LEVEL OF HUSTLE:

Don't bother telling the world you are ready. Show it. Do it.

Peter Dinklage

DATE:

How I'm Gonna Crush My Goals Today:

....

....

....

....

....

....

....

....

....

....

....

....

TODAY'S LEVEL OF HUSTLE:

☐   ☐   ☐    ☐

I know how it looks. But just start. Nothing is insurmountable.

Lin-Manuel Miranda

How I'm Gonna Crush My Goals Today:

If you run into a wall, don't turn around and give up. Figure out how to climb it, go through it, or work around it.

Michael Jordan

DATE:

How I'm Gonna Crush My Goals Today:

....

....

....

....

....

....

....

....

....

....

....

TODAY'S LEVEL OF HUSTLE:

My father used to say to me, "The only limit to your success is your own imagination." I actually believed that—like, I'm still coming to terms with the fact that I might not be an Olympic figure skater.

Shonda Rhimes

DATE:

How I'm Gonna Crush My Goals Today:

....

....

....

....

....

....

....

....

....

....

....

....

....

TODAY'S LEVEL OF HUSTLE:

☐    ☐   ☐   ☐

Remember to look up at the stars and not down at your feet … However difficult life may seem, there is always something you can do and succeed at. It matters that you don't just give up.

Stephen Hawking

DATE:

How I'm Gonna Crush My Goals Today:

....

....

....

....

....

....

....

....

....

....

....

....

TODAY'S LEVEL OF HUSTLE:

☐   ☐   ☐    ☐

I wondered about the explorers who'd sailed their ships to the end of the world. How terrified they must have been when they risked falling over the edge; how amazed to discover, instead, places they had seen only in their dreams.

Jodi Picoult

DATE:

— How I'm Gonna Crush My Goals Today: —

....

....

....

....

....

....

....

....

....

....

....

....

TODAY'S LEVEL OF HUSTLE:

I believe in the person I want to become.

Lana del Rey

DATE:

How I'm Gonna Crush My Goals Today:

....

....

....

....

....

....

....

....

....

....

....

....

TODAY'S LEVEL OF HUSTLE:

☐   ☐    ☐   ☐

When you're in your lane, there's no traffic.

Ava DuVernay

How I'm Gonna Crush My Goals Today:

 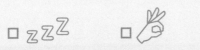

If people say your dreams are crazy, if people laugh at what you think you can do, good. Stay that way. Because what nonbelievers fail to understand is that calling a dream crazy is not an insult. It's a compliment.

Colin Kaepernick

How I'm Gonna Crush My Goals Today:

....

....

....

....

....

....

....

....

....

....

....

TODAY'S LEVEL OF HUSTLE:

☐ 　　☐ 　　☐ 　　☐

Do not confuse dreams with wishes. There is a difference. Dreams are where you visualize yourself being successful at what's important to you to accomplish. And dreams build convictions.

Dolly Parton

DATE:

How I'm Gonna Crush My Goals Today:

....

....

....

....

....

....

....

....

....

....

....

....

....

TODAY'S LEVEL OF HUSTLE:

If I'm shinin', everybody gonna shine (yeah, I'm goals)

I was born like this, don't even gotta try.

Lizzo

DATE:

How I'm Gonna Crush My Goals Today:

....

....

....

....

....

....

....

....

....

....

....

....

TODAY'S LEVEL OF HUSTLE:

Life is a succession of moments. To live each one is to succeed.

Corita Kent

DATE:

How I'm Gonna Crush My Goals Today:

TODAY'S LEVEL OF HUSTLE:

It really is a test of: How bad you wanna do this? I had to remind myself every day that I didn't want to do anything else and that I was good enough to do it.

Issa Rae

DATE:

How I'm Gonna Crush My Goals Today:

Baby steps. Baby steps. Baby steps through the office. Baby steps out the door. It works. It works! All I have to do is take one little step at a time, and I can do anything.

Bob (what about Bob?)

DATE:

How I'm Gonna Crush My Goals Today:

....

....

....

....

....

....

....

....

....

....

....

....

TODAY'S LEVEL OF HUSTLE:

I am so smart.
I am so smart.
I am so smart.
I am so smart.
S-M-R-T—
I mean S-M-A-R-T.

Homer Simpson

How I'm Gonna Crush My Goals Today:

TODAY'S LEVEL OF HUSTLE:

☐ zᶻᶻ ☐  ☐ ☐

I'm not goal-oriented so much as I'm constantly aware of what I'm passionate about, and I'm constantly updating the list.

Greta Gerwig

DATE:

How I'm Gonna Crush My Goals Today:

....

....

....

....

....

....

....

....

....

....

....

....

....

....

....

....

....

....

TODAY'S LEVEL OF HUSTLE:

☐   ☐   ☐    ☐

I live my best life in celebration mode. My performance in the World Cup was good, but I was thinking all along, Just wait until I get to the celebrations.

Megan Rapinoe

DATE:

How I'm Gonna Crush My Goals Today:

Power's not given to you. You have to take it.

Beyoncé

DATE:

How I'm Gonna Crush My Goals Today:

....

....

....

....

....

....

....

....

....

....

....

....

....

TODAY'S LEVEL OF HUSTLE:

☐    ☐   ☐   ☐

Sometimes you just have to put on lip gloss and pretend to be psyched.

Mindy Kaling

DATE:

How I'm Gonna Crush My Goals Today:

....

....

....

....

....

....

....

....

....

....

....

....

TODAY'S LEVEL OF HUSTLE:

□   □   □   □

Great people do things before they are ready. They do things before they know they can do it. Doing what you're afraid of, getting out of your comfort zone, taking risks—that's what life is.

Amy Poehler

How I'm Gonna Crush My Goals Today:

....

....

....

....

....

....

....

....

....

....

....

....

TODAY'S LEVEL OF HUSTLE:

If adversity makes you stronger, I think I'm the Hulk at this point.

Lindsey Vonn

DATE:

How I'm Gonna Crush My Goals Today:

....

....

....

....

....

....

....

....

....

....

....

....

TODAY'S LEVEL OF HUSTLE:

Start before you're ready. Don't prepare, begin.

Mel Robbins

DATE:

How I'm Gonna Crush My Goals Today:

....

....

....

....

....

....

....

....

....

....

....

....

TODAY'S LEVEL OF HUSTLE:

□   □   □   □

Build your own pyramids, write your own hieroglyphs.

Kendrick Lamar

How I'm Gonna Crush My Goals Today:

....

....

....

....

....

....

....

....

....

....

....

TODAY'S LEVEL OF HUSTLE:

Be ready to pay the price of your dreams. Free cheese can only be found in a mousetrap.

Paulo Coelho

DATE:

How I'm Gonna Crush My Goals Today:

....

....

....

....

....

....

....

....

....

....

....

....

....

....

TODAY'S LEVEL OF HUSTLE:

  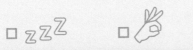

You can't be that kid standing at the top of the waterslide, overthinking it. You have to go down the chute.

Tina Fey

How I'm Gonna Crush My Goals Today:

....

....

....

....

....

....

....

....

....

....

....

TODAY'S LEVEL OF HUSTLE:

□   □   □    □

Live every week like it's Shark Week.

Tracy Jordan (30 Rock)

DATE:

How I'm Gonna Crush My Goals Today:

....

....

....

....

....

....

....

....

....

....

....

....

TODAY'S LEVEL OF HUSTLE:

Fortune favors the brave.

DATE:

How I'm Gonna Crush My Goals Today:

....

....

....

....

....

....

....

....

....

....

....

....

TODAY'S LEVEL OF HUSTLE:

☐   ☐   ☐    ☐

Once I had asked God for one or two extra inches in height, but instead he made me as tall as the sky, so high that I could not measure myself.

Malala Yousafzai

DATE:

How I'm Gonna Crush My Goals Today:

You will never hear more people tell you that you're wrong than when you're succeeding.

Grimes

How I'm Gonna Crush My Goals Today:

TODAY'S LEVEL OF HUSTLE:

My ambition is to enjoy my life and to do exactly what I want to do. And I'll do that. I will be free.

Venus Williams

DATE:

How I'm Gonna Crush My Goals Today:

....

....

....

....

....

....

....

....

....

....

....

TODAY'S LEVEL OF HUSTLE:

□   □    □   □

Why, sometimes I've believed as many as six impossible things before breakfast.

Lewis Carroll

DATE:

How I'm Gonna Crush My Goals Today:

....

....

....

....

....

....

....

....

....

....

....

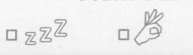

You can't wait for inspiration. You have to go after it with a club.

Jack London

DATE:

How I'm Gonna Crush My Goals Today:

....

....

....

....

....

....

....

....

....

....

....

TODAY'S LEVEL OF HUSTLE:

☐   ☐   ☐   ☐

At first people refuse to believe that a strange new thing can be done, then they begin to hope it can be done, then they see it can be done … and all the world wonders why it was not done centuries ago.

Frances Hodgson Burnett

DATE:

How I'm Gonna Crush My Goals Today:

....

....

....

....

....

....

....

....

....

....

....

....

TODAY'S LEVEL OF HUSTLE:

☐   ☐   ☐   ☐

Sometimes you gotta work a little, so you can ball a lot.

Tom (Parks and Recreation)

How I'm Gonna Crush My Goals Today:

....

....

....

....

....

....

....

....

....

....

....

....

TODAY'S LEVEL OF HUSTLE:

When I write . . . I'm free. And I can do whatever I want on the page and nothing can hold me down. And I love that.

Roxane Gay

DATE:

How I'm Gonna Crush My Goals Today:

....

....

....

....

....

....

....

....

....

....

....

....

....

TODAY'S LEVEL OF HUSTLE:

    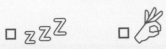

You are on the eve of a complete victory. You can't go wrong. The world is behind you.

Josephine Baker

DATE:

How I'm Gonna Crush My Goals Today:

....

....

....

....

....

....

....

....

....

....

....

....

....

TODAY'S LEVEL OF HUSTLE:

☐   ☐  ☐   ☐

I am who I am, doing what I came to do.

Audre Lorde

DATE:

How I'm Gonna Crush My Goals Today:

....

....

....

....

....

....

....

....

....

....

....

....

....

TODAY'S LEVEL OF HUSTLE:

We choose to go to the moon in this decade and do the other things, not because they are easy, but because they are hard.

John F. Kennedy

DATE:

How I'm Gonna Crush My Goals Today:

....

....

....

....

....

....

....

....

....

....

....

....

....

....

....

....

....

TODAY'S LEVEL OF HUSTLE:

☐ 　　☐ 　　☐ 　　☐

You can settle for reality, or you can go off, like a fool, and dream another dream.

Nora Ephron

DATE:

How I'm Gonna Crush My Goals Today:

....

....

....

....

....

....

....

....

....

....

....

....

TODAY'S LEVEL OF HUSTLE:

☐   ☐   ☐    ☐

We showed that we are united and that we, young people, are unstoppable.

Greta Thunberg

DATE:

How I'm Gonna Crush My Goals Today:

....

....

....

....

....

....

....

....

....

....

....

....

TODAY'S LEVEL OF HUSTLE:

☐   ☐    ☐   ☐

Life loves to be taken by the lapel and told: "I'm with you kid. Let's go."

Maya Angelou

How I'm Gonna Crush My Goals Today:

TODAY'S LEVEL OF HUSTLE:

She must find a boat and sail in it. No guarantee of shore. Only a conviction that what she wanted could exist, if she dared to find it.

Jeanette Winterson

How I'm Gonna Crush My Goals Today:

....

....

....

....

....

....

....

....

....

....

....

....

TODAY'S LEVEL OF HUSTLE:

You never know if you can actually do something against all odds until you actually do it.

Abby Wambach

DATE:

How I'm Gonna Crush My Goals Today:

....

....

....

....

....

....

....

....

....

....

....

....

....

TODAY'S LEVEL OF HUSTLE:

Nobody who ever accomplished anything big or new or worth raising a celebratory fist in the air did it from their comfort zone. They risked ridicule and failure and sometimes even death.

Jen Sincero

How I'm Gonna Crush My Goals Today:

TODAY'S LEVEL OF HUSTLE:

I dwell in Possibility.

Emily Dickinson

DATE:

How I'm Gonna Crush My Goals Today:

....

....

....

....

....

....

....

....

....

....

....

....

....

....

....

....

....

....

TODAY'S LEVEL OF HUSTLE:

□   □    □   □

A career is built one paragraph at a time. I wrote six books and a blue-million articles before anything of mine hit the bestseller lists. I don't know any shortcuts.

Barbara Kingsolver

DATE:

How I'm Gonna Crush My Goals Today:

....

....

....

....

....

....

....

....

....

....

....

....

TODAY'S LEVEL OF HUSTLE:

 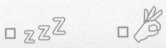

The only way to get a thing done is to start to do it, then keep on doing it, and finally you'll finish it, even if in the beginning you think you can't do it at all.

Langston Hughes

DATE:

How I'm Gonna Crush My Goals Today:

....

....

....

....

....

....

....

....

....

....

....

....

TODAY'S LEVEL OF HUSTLE:

☐   ☐   ☐   ☐

There is no easy way to the stars from earth.

Seneca

How I'm Gonna Crush My Goals Today:

....

....

....

....

....

....

....

....

....

....

....

....

....

....

....

....

....

TODAY'S LEVEL OF HUSTLE:

□   □   □    □

We're the authors of our lives. When we own our story, we get to write the ending.

Brené Brown

How I'm Gonna Crush My Goals Today:

TODAY'S LEVEL OF HUSTLE:

I got my first guitar when I was nine because I wanted to be the fifth Beatle, even though they had already broken up.

Tig Notaro

How I'm Gonna Crush My Goals Today:

TODAY'S LEVEL OF HUSTLE:

You must put your head into the lion's mouth if the performance is to be a success.

Winston Churchill

DATE:

How I'm Gonna Crush My Goals Today:

....

....

....

....

....

....

....

....

....

....

....

....

TODAY'S LEVEL OF HUSTLE:

☐ 　☐ 　☐ 　☐

This is the fast lane, folks . . . and some of us like it here.

Hunter S. Thompson

DATE:

How I'm Gonna Crush My Goals Today:

....

....

....

....

....

....

....

....

....

....

....

....

TODAY'S LEVEL OF HUSTLE:

☐   ☐    ☐   ☐

Embrace the ever changing, ever evolving world with the best rule I've ever found. Say "YES AND."

Jane Lynch

DATE:

How I'm Gonna Crush My Goals Today:

 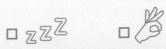

I'll eat some breakfast, then change the world.

John Waters (Hairspray)

DATE:

How I'm Gonna Crush My Goals Today:

Dumbo didn't need the feather; the magic was in him.

Stephen King

How I'm Gonna Crush My Goals Today:

You're a total rock star.

Knock Knock